HARRIET AND THE PROMISED LAND

by JACOB LAWRENCE

WINDMILL BOOKS, INC. ■ **SIMON & SCHUSTER, INC., NEW YORK**

To the courageous women
of America

Published by Windmill Books, Inc./Simon & Schuster, Inc.
Rockefeller Center, 630 Fifth Avenue
New York, New York 10020

First Printing

Library of Congress Catalog Card Number: 68-25752
Manufactured in the United States of America

This is the story of Harriet Tubman, born a slave in Maryland in 1822, who made a daring escape to the North and freedom. At the risk of her life she returned nineteen times to lead over three hundred of her people to "The Promised Land."

Harriet, Harriet,
Born a slave.

Work for your master

From your cradle
To your grave.

Harriet, clean,
Harriet, sweep.
Harriet, rock
The child to sleep.

Harriet, hear tell
About the Promised Land,
How Moses led the slaves
Over Egypt's sand.

How Pharaoh's heart
Was hard as stone.
How the Lord told Moses
He was not alone.

Harriet, pray
To the Lord at night
For strength to free your people
When the time is right.

Harriet, grow bigger.
Harriet, grow stronger.
Harriet, work harder.
Harriet, work longer.

Then . . .
Harriet got the sign
That the time was right.
She cried, "Brothers! Sisters!
I'll lead you tonight!"

The North Star shone
To light Harriet's way,

And they marched by night,
And they slept by day.

Some were afraid,
But none turned back,
For close at their heels
Howled the bloodhound pack.

A snake said, "Hiss!"
An owl said, "Whoo!"
Harriet said, "We are
Coming through!"

A runaway slave
With a price on her head,
"I'll be free," said Harriet,
"Or I'll be dead!"

She said, "Believe in the Lord!"
She said, "Believe in me!"
She said, "Brothers! Sisters!
We're going to be free!"

They slept in a barn
With the barnyard fowl.
And Harriet kept watch
Like a barnyard owl.

Good people gave
Them food to eat
And a chance to rest
Their weary feet.

They gave Harriet chickens
To disguise
The runaway slave
From spying eyes.

Then the north wind howled
Like a bloodhound pack.
But none were afraid,
And none turned back.

Harriet led them 'cross the snow
Toward the Promised Land
As Moses led his people
'Cross the burning sand.

They marched through the cold,
They marched through the heat.
And the only sound
Was their marching feet.
Now they marched by day,
Now they marched by night,
Still the Promised Land
Was not in sight.
Now Harriet grew weary
And sick at heart.
Now the Lord
Sent Harriet
A chariot!

The chariot was sent
By the Lord's Own Hand,

And Harriet
Rode the chariot
To the Promised Land!

Harriet, Harriet,
Born to be free,
Led her people
To liberty!